Yoga for Cats

(those adorable felines who only want to get better and better...if that's even possible)

Meet the teacher

This is an
utterly silly book
BUT
an utterly TRUE account!
Ladies: take note!
(gentlemen too)

Yoga for Cats

Illustrated by Kath Walker

MQP

Introduction

The practice of yoga provides us with a great way to stay in shape both in mind and body. Although, clearly, cats are not actually able to perform any of the exercises shown here – and nor should they be encouraged to – their sleek, flexible bodies and their elegant, graceful movements do offer us mere humans an invaluable insight into how to remedy our own awkward gestures.

Yoga offers us the opportunity to improve our flexibility, strength, breath control, posture and balance.

It teaches us the wisdom both of getting more in touch with who we really are, strengthening and refining our physical bodies while also focussing and concentrating the mind.

Without a doubt, regular yoga sessions can greatly reduce our stress levels and improve our feelings of wellbeing, leaving us all purring contentedly.

...Meet the girls...

Bitsy

Muffy

Fashion guru

Social butterfly

Charlie

(yes, she's a girl)

Attitude issues

So...one fine day everything seems not so fine...

Darlings, my nerves are shattered! It's all too, too terrible...everything's going wrong! I'm feeling like a furry feline failure.

So...later on that same over-indulgent chocolate day... Bitsy, while devouring her current issue of **Catnip** (along with an extra rich double fudge brownie) comes across an article on...you guessed it...

...Yoga!

Sweetie pie...you'll never guess...we're all going to yoga class...why? Well to discover our true physical and spiritual selves...you know...get in touch with our inner kitten...

So after a few anxious heartbeats and trepidations they arrive...

The first class with Madame Omm

Love her outfit.

First we breathe, just watch and learn. Imagine, my dears, breathe and then... better posture, that means strength, unbelievable stamina! You can be a match for any four-pawed canine!

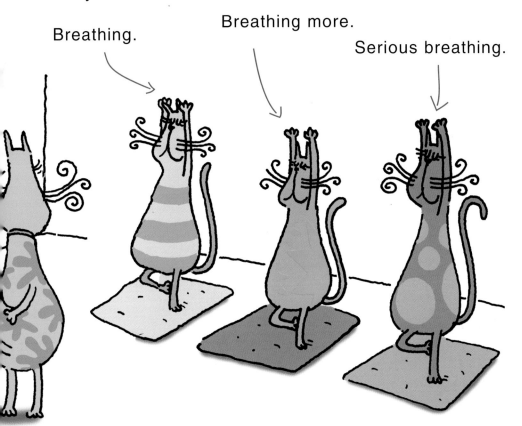

So the Kitty Kapers...

...begin in earnest....

This is what we call meditation.
So fix your minds on the pose.
Breathe into the tension, release, release, release…
then think nothing.

…nothing…

…nothing…

…nothing?

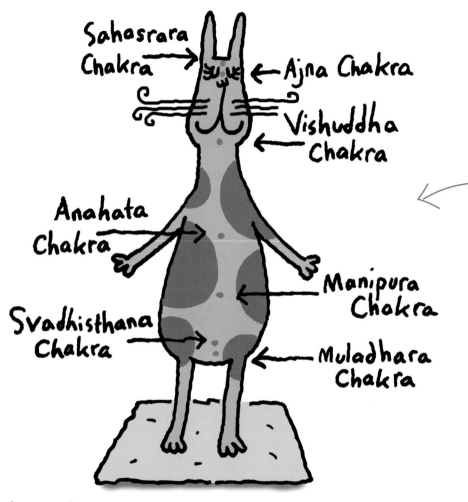

Sahasrara Chakra

Ajna Chakra

Vishuddha Chakra

Anahata Chakra

Manipura Chakra

Svadhisthana Chakra

Muladhara Chakra

Ladies, here are your seven energy channels.

Deepen your thoughts.

Be in the moment.

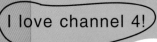

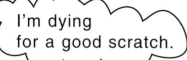

The Hero

My hero...my hero is...is...is

Watch this teach…

If I had a ball of yarn I'd roll it up to the top of the stairs…

…then I'd roll it down again…

The Tree - Lengthen the spine, reach for the sky.
Hold that. Feel taller, ladies.

The Cobra

The Downward Facing Dog

The Bow

I have always loved every bow they put on me, especially the cute one with bells I wear for birthdays.

The Plank

Did you know the smallest feline is a masterpiece?

I'm quite sure that if I just lie here long enough...the world will quietly reshape itself for my convenience!

Now The Forward Stretch, my darlings. Stretching is a beautiful thing...just reach out, that's right, breathe...

Now assume the Lotus Position. This is a classical position used in meditation. It is one of the most difficult to master but once mastered …it is one of the most relaxing.

yoga for cats | 65

The Shoulder Stand

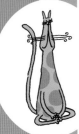

And now The Fish

The fish! The fish!

The Corpse ~ just rest...oh dear...I hear kitty snores...

So they finished their first session...

Good spirits are flying!

So...back they go for...you guessed it – *advanced Yoga!*

...and totally **advanced**...

...pussycat pleasure!

Published by MQ Publications Limited

12 The Ivories, 6–8 Northampton Street

London N1 2HY

Tel: +44 (0) 20 7359 2244

Fax:+44 (0) 20 7359 1616

email: mail@mqpublications.com

website: www.mqpublications.com

Copyright © MQ Publications Limited 2004

Illustrations © Kath Walker

ISBN: 1-84072-530-3

10 9 8 7 6 5 4 3 2 1

Printed and bound in China